BRIGHT AND BEAUTIFUL
MAKING YOUR OWN NATURAL COSMETICS

by Brennan et al.

*"the book the cosmetics industry
doesn't want you to have"*

SAFETY NOTICE:

If you have a medical condition, or are pregnant, none of the information in this book should be followed without first consulting a doctor.
All safety guidelines, warnings and instructions should be read carefully before following any recipes. Some recipes call for the use of allergens such as nut oils. Do not use in the case of a known allergy and always conduct a patch test prior to application.
See page 83 for full safety advice on using essential oils.
There are no preservatives in any of these products. If you wish to prolong the shelf life of your creations, you will need to source a suitable preservative. We recommend using a broad spectrum preservative and sterilising all of your ingredients and equipment prior to making, as this will also inhibit mould and bacteria growth. Each recipe offers a guide of how long the product will last unpreserved.
The publisher cannot accept any responsibility for injuries or damage caused by failure to comply with any of the guidelines in this book.

Copyright © 2018 Tender Essence
Author © David Brennan (see page 94 for acknowledgments)

1st Edition

ISBN 978-1-83853-046-4

Printed in England

"The Earth laughs in flowers."
- Ralph Waldo Emerson

BRIGHT AND BEAUTIFUL
MAKING YOUR OWN NATURAL COSMETICS

by Brennan et al.

*"the book the cosmetics industry
doesn't want you to have"*

INTRODUCTION

Being a consumer has never been so overwhelming. Every day we are forced to choose between shelves upon shelves of products, attempting to compare their ethical values, environmental impact, quality and price to find the best option for us. Millions of animals continue to be tested on yearly for the cosmetics industry. The home fragrance industry contributes to an already staggering amount of plastic and air pollution. Various potentially damaging chemicals are being added to seemingly harmless beauty products. It's becoming dangerous to value convenience over ethics.

However, there is an easier way. The most important part of our journey towards conscious living is simply getting started. Small steps are better than no steps. With this book by your side you will be empowered to create an endless supply of vegan products for a happy body and natural home. No animal testing. No unnecessary packaging. No harmful ingredients.

Just naturally beautiful products created with the most important person in mind: **You.**

Contents

WHAT YOU WILL NEED

THE BASICS

We know you're raring to get started on your journey towards natural living and that it's tempting to skip straight to the recipes. So, we promise to keep this bit simple. Not only will reading this section save you time in the long run, it will set you up for homemade greatness. It's not complicated, but it is important. To get you off on the right foot we're going to run you through the equipment and ingredients you will need. At the back of the book you can find the safety information that is important to keep in mind, as well as the basics of aromatherapy and essential oils.

EQUIPMENT

Don't worry, we're not expecting you to invest in a bunch of specialist equipment. We're trying to free you from constantly buying, not force you into buying more! Most of these items will already be in your kitchen and are easy to use. However, if you do need to invest in certain items such as a thermometer or electric hand whisk, they really needn't be expensive. Cheap items with the most basic of settings will get the job done just as well as higher range products.

Utensils Needed

Silicone ice cube or small baking moulds

Two part moulds (craft baubles may be cheaper and will work just as well!)

Airtight containers

Microwave

Hob and pan

Electric hand whisk

Blender (you will only need this in one recipe)

Mixing spoons

Large mixing bowl

Electric kitchen scales

Measuring spoons

Funnel

Large microwavable measuring jug

Thermometer (you will only need this in one recipe)

Packaging For Your Products

For most of these recipes you won't even need to buy new containers. Old jam jars, empty twist-up lip balm tubes and used product bottles are all you need. If you do invest in anything though, bottles with spray and dropper tops are handy to have around.

Once you've got into the swing of making your own products it's only natural to start thinking about giving them as gifts, or even selling them. That's when packaging becomes more important. There are many ways of up-cycling old containers. Here are a few ideas:

1. Mason Jars: Mason jars are a great way to store your products and are easy to customise. Covering them in matt paint and then distressing parts of the jars with sandpaper can create a shabby chic look. Or simply wrap ribbon around the neck of the jar to add some colour.

2. Labels: Adding labels to products is essential when giving them to someone else, to remind them how to use it and what the main ingredients are. Either use simple brown paper tags and string or get extra fancy with chalk board stickers.

3. Charity Shop Finds: Second hand shops may have a wealth of ornate bottles and jars to make your creations look even more fancy. At only a few pounds a purchase, it's hard to say no!

4. Filling: If you decide to put your products in a box, it's important to protect them using packaging filler. Bubble wrap or styrofoam adds to your plastic consumption, so why not use torn up newspaper or magazines?

5. Ribbon: It can make anything look luxurious, but ribbon can get expensive if you're using it regularly. Cutting old pieces of clothing into strips can be a great, rustic alternative.

INGREDIENTS

The best part about making homemade cosmetics and fragrances is that you don't need to add in any of the harsh chemicals that are often used by large companies. Trust us, your skin will thank you for it! Most of the ingredients we use throughout the book are household items or are easy to get hold of. We have been careful with ingredients that aren't common, to use the same ones in as many recipes as possible. That way, you're only making one investment and will get used to working with them.

ESSENTIAL OILS

There's a reason that essential oils have been used within societies for centuries. The list of their cosmetic and therapeutic uses is seemingly endless and we continue to be amazed by the ways that they can be used in everyday life. This is the reason that essential oils form the foundation for these recipes. Using them will empower you to create natural products that will not only benefit your skin and hair, but also your emotional wellbeing.

Once extracted from plants and seeds through a process of distillation, essential oils form a highly volatile substance. This means that they transition quickly from a liquid to a gas, vaporising at room temperature and dispersing their scent. When used in these DIYs they add the fragrance of the plant that they were extracted from with just a few drops.

In this book we use 26 essential oils, which you can find more information about on page 84. You won't need all of them, as you can swap and change the oils in these recipes to create products personal to you.

Essential oils are for topical use only. Find our full safety guide on page 83.

CARRIER OILS AND MOISTURISERS

Also known as base oils, carrier oils are used to dilute essential oils to make them safe for application to the skin. However, all of the carrier oils that we use have the added benefit of being moisturising and nourishing. In most recipes they are interchangeable with any virgin or raw oils that you have in your home. Just be careful not to substitute oils that are solid at room temperature for those that are not. The two main carrier oils that we suggest are coconut oil and grapeseed oil, although sweet almond oil and avocado are two luxurious potential additions to your collection.

EMULSIFIERS

For the sake of simplicity and saving you money, we only use one emulsifier in this book. In fact, emulsifiers are often not needed and products can simply be shaken before application. However, perfumes and room sprays do need a little bit more attention to ensure that fragrance is dispersed evenly. Our choice of emulsifier is Polysorbate 20. We know it sounds scary, but it is simply used to combine water and oil-based substances.

Bath and Shower Products

Our bath and shower products use more ingredients that are not oil-based, but we have been careful to find the most economical and environmentally friendly options. We have used the vegan-friendly setting agent 'agar-agar', although this can be swapped for other plant-based alternatives.

Finally, you may need to raid your baking cupboard for bicarbonate of soda or get down to your local health store for Epsom Salts.

Candles and Soaps

Perhaps the only crafts that require more specialist ingredients and equipment are soap and candle making. Although it takes some practice, it is well worth it for the end result. For the sake of ease and safety we highly recommend melt-and-pour solutions when making soap, which can easily be purchased online or in craft stores. When making candles, you will need to invest in soy wax flakes and wicks. However, when bought in bulk these kinds of ingredients will last you a long time.

TOPPINGS

Throughout this book we share with you different basic ideas and recipes for making cosmetics and gifts. Similar to baking a cake, you can then add your own theme or style to it, through additions, toppings and decorations. What you can add depends on how well the item can hold them. For example, some colourings don't work with candles but would work with soap, while adding dried flowers might be appropriate for a bath bomb, but not for a body lotion. Furthermore, it depends on who the product is intended for - it all comes down to personal choice, suitability and how well the additions will work with the existing ingredients.

Toppings are possibly the easiest thing to add - simply grate or sprinkle something over the top to complement the product. Make sure you consider how the item will be used - it's fine to add lavender flowers to a lavender soap, as long as you don't mind them ending up in your bath. Some things you can easily add are orange zest, which adds scent and colour, sugar, salt or poppy seeds for exfoliation, or dried flowers, which can look very pretty. If you don't have easy access to any flowers, the contents of a herbal tea bag make a great alternative.

COLOURINGS

Since this book is all about natural cosmetics, we won't be giving any examples of micas or manufactured chemical dyes. Luckily, there are plenty of plants and roots that can be used to produce colours - the Egyptians and Incas have been using them for centuries! They aren't always as bright, but they will be natural and safe.

All of the following can be heated in oil to produce a coloured oil for use in your products:

Beetroot Powder = Red   **Cambrian Blue Clay** = Pastel Blue/Grey
Paprika = Orange   **Alkanet Root** = Purple
Turmeric = Yellow   **French Pink Clay** = Pastel Pink
Spirulina Powder = Green   **Activated Charcoal** = Dark Grey
French Green Clay = Green/Grey   **Alkanet Root + Charcoal** = Almost Black

THE RECIPES

THE FACE

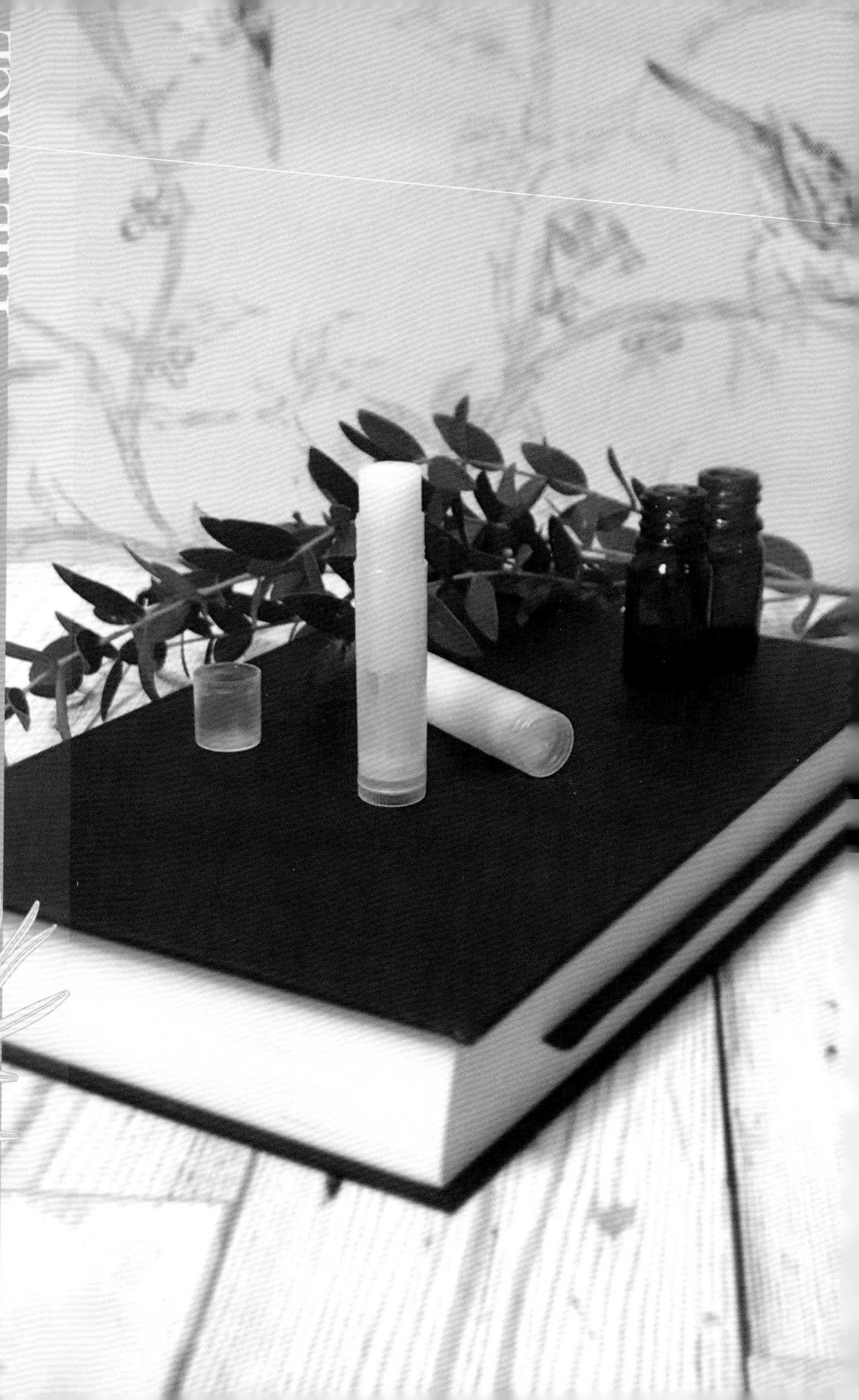

Tea Tree Spot Stick

Spots are unfortunately a fact of life that most of us have to put up with at some point.

Whether it's puberty, PMS or simply water intake, there are many factors that contribute to the quality of our skin. But that doesn't mean you have to splash out on a range of expensive products to combat any pimple parties.

Tea tree has been used for generations thanks to its antiviral, antibacterial and anti-fungal properties. This spot stick makes targeting specific areas of the skin easy, without the harsh chemicals that are often added to conventional products.

Ingredients:

Cosmetic grade pillar soy wax 30g
Coconut oil 30g
Shea butter 2g
Tea tree essential oil 1 tsp (5ml)

Equipment:

Microwavable jug
Metal spoon
Empty twist up lip balm tubes 2-3

Method:

1. Place the coconut oil and soy wax in your jug and microwave in 5 second intervals until completely liquid.

2. Quickly stir in the tea tree oil until thoroughly combined.

3. Leave the mixture to cool slightly before adding the shea butter.

4. Carefully pour the mixture into your lip balm tubes (twisted fully down), then leave them in a cool dry place to fully set.

5. Once set, store the tubes in the fridge to avoid the product melting. Use within 12 months.

CLAY AND TEA TREE FACE MASK

Face masks are a great way to draw out impurities and should be a staple in every skincare routine.

With its mix of bentonite clay and witch hazel, this tightening mask is the ultimate facial detox. The addition of tea tree oil makes it even better at keeping spots at bay.
We recommend using the mask once or twice a week to keep you blemish free and glowing. Be sure to use non-metallic utensils when making the mask. Contact with metal causes the clay to lose its negative charge, stopping it from drawing out impurities effectively.

Ingredients:
Bentonite clay 15g
Witch hazel with alcohol 1 tbsp (15ml)
Tea tree essential oil 3 drops
Equipment:
Non-metallic spoon
Glass bowl

Method:

1. Put the clay into your bowl, add the witch hazel and stir until it is smooth. The mixture will fizz at first - this is nothing to worry about.

2. Mix in the tea tree oil until all three ingredients are combined.

3. Using your fingers, apply the mask to cleansed skin and leave it on until completely dry.

4. Rinse the mask off with warm water. Your skin may flush slightly as the mask draws blood to the surface. Use immediately as this product will set.

Helpful Hint: This mask can also be used to combat back or chest acne.

SOOTHING LAVENDER AFTERSHAVE BALM

This whipped aftershave balm is perfect for use on both the face and the legs, with its soothing and moisturising properties.

Coconut oil and almond oil combine to counteract the drying effect that shaving can have, whilst lavender stops any potential itching. When complete the balm has a whipped consistency and a sweet-woody scent that is absolutely irresistible.

Ingredients:
Coconut oil 250g
Almond oil 2 tsp (10ml)
Cedarwood essential oil 7 drops
Lavender essential oil 7 drops
Equipment:
Electric whisk
Bowl
Jar or airtight container

Method:

1. Whip the coconut oil using an electric whisk on the lowest setting for about 3 minutes until smooth.

2. Add the remainder of the ingredients and whisk for an extra 2 minutes.

3. Store in an airtight jar and smooth over the skin after shaving as needed. Use within 6 months.

APPLE AND FRANKINCENSE ANTI-AGING CREAM

Frankincense is a powerful astringent that protects skin cells and prevents wrinkles, making it the star ingredient of this anti-aging cream.

When combined with vitamin filled apples and the fatty acids of avocado oil, the cream leaves skin plump and deeply moisturised.

As this is a heavier cream, we recommend applying it as the last step in your skincare routine before bed. By morning it will have worked its magic, leaving you looking and feeling baby smooth.

Ingredients:
Rose water 4 tbsp (60ml)
Avocado oil 1 tbsp (15ml)
Frankincense essential oil 6 drops
Apples 2

Equipment:
Blender
Hob and pan
Knife

Method:

1. Core and slice the apples into small chunks and place into the blender.

2. Add the avocado oil and blend until the mixture forms a smooth paste.

3. Heat the apple mixture over the hob on a low heat for approximately 10 minutes, stirring frequently.

4. Remove from the heat and add the rose water, mixing until combined.

5. Allow to cool for a few minutes and then add the frankincense.

6. Leave the mixture to fully cool before transferring it to an air tight container and storing it in the fridge. Use within 5 days.

LAVENDER AND TEA TREE FACIAL TONER

Toners are often overlooked in the skincare world, but can seriously improve the quality of your skin.

When used daily after cleansing this one can help to restore natural pH levels, shrink pores and refresh the skin in one sweep. Just dab onto cotton wool and wipe over the face for that natural glow.

The anti-inflammatory properties of lavender combined with spot fighting tea tree make this the perfect step before moisturising. Furthermore, witch hazel removes excess oils to prevent future breakouts.

Ingredients:
Witch hazel with alcohol 90ml
Lavender essential oil 10 drops
Tea tree essential oil 5 drops
Equipment:
Spray glass bottle

Method:

1. Combine the essential oils in your bottle, screw on the lid and shake well.

2. Add the witch hazel and shake again until thoroughly mixed.

3. Spray the toner directly from the bottle or soak into cotton wool to apply. Use within 3 months.

BEARD OIL

We all know that we should look after the hair on our heads, but facial hair often gets overlooked.

An oil is essential in any bearded man's self-care kit, to keep it tidy, moisturised and smelling gorgeous. Applying a few drops of this daily before brushing or combing is the perfect finishing touch to your routine and will stop any itching. The base notes of cedarwood and frankincense create a masculine, woody combination that will stay with you throughout the day, without being overpowering. Whether for yourself or to give as a gift, this is a simple but nourishing DIY.

Ingredients:
Sweet almond oil 2 tbsp (30ml)
Cedarwood essential oil 3 drops
Frankincense essential oil 3 drops
Equipment:
Small glass bottle (preferably with dropper)

Method:

1. Simply combine the sweet almond oil and essential oils in your bottle, screw the cap on and shake to combine.

2. Make sure that the oil is thoroughly mixed before every use.

3. Apply a small amount to your fingertips and then onto your beard. Comb through if necessary. Use within 6 months.

The Recipes

The Body

Detoxifying Foot Soak

With the botanical name "Citrus Paradisi", grapefruit oil really is paradise for your feet.

Its invigorating scent and anti-fungal properties make it the perfect remedy for tired tootsies. Frankincense is known as a natural deodoriser and Epsom salts relax the joints and muscles. So, whether you've been in heels or running shoes, this foot soak is exactly what you need at the end of a busy day.

Ingredients:
Epsom salt 250g
Sea salt 250g
Baking soda 150g
Grapefruit essential oil 1/2 tbsp (7.5ml)
Clary sage essential oil 1/2 tsp (2.5ml)
Equipment:
Airtight container

Method:

1. Simply combine all of the ingredients, ensuring that the oils are distributed evenly.

2. When needed, use roughly 1/4 of the mixture in a bowl of warm water and soak your feet for 15 minutes, or as long as desired.

3. Use within 1 month and store in a dry place.

Sensual Massage Oil

Studies have shown that skin on skin contact releases a small amount of oxytocin in the brain, which helps us to feel more confident and to bond.

This explains why touch can have such a huge impact on our mood, particularly in regards to sexual experiences. Taking the time to enjoy giving and receiving a sensual massage and encouraging the release of oxytocin can pave the way for stronger and longer orgasms.
Ylang ylang is a soothing scent that will help you to let go of tension, whilst clary sage boosts the libido. The best part is that this massage oil is extremely simple to make, meaning less time in the kitchen and more time in the bedroom!

Ingredients:
Sweet almond oil 2 tbsp (30ml)
Ylang ylang essential oil 5 drops
Clary sage essential oil 5 drops
Equipment:
Small glass bottle

Method:

1. Mix all of the ingredients together until completely combined.

2. Pour the massage oil into your bottle and store out of direct sunlight.

3. To use, simply apply to hands before massaging onto the skin (yours or somebody else's!). This oil is for external use only. Use within 6 months.

DREAMY LAVENDER AND ORANGE LOTION

Lavender and orange oils are the perfect companions for bedtime bliss.

Whilst lavender is well known for its calming effect, orange can have the benefit of reducing anxieties before sleep. This body lotion contains shea butter, which is perfect for use after a long soak in the bath to moisturise the skin. Simply rub this all over your body before bed, pop on your PJs and wake up in the morning with beautifully smooth skin.

Ingredients:
Shea butter 125g
Sweet almond oil 2 tbsp (30ml)
Lavender essential oil 10 drops
Orange essential oil 5 drops
Equipment:
Large bowl
Electric whisk
Jar or pump container

Method:

1. Combine the shea butter and sweet almond oil in a bowl.

2. Whisk the mixture until it reaches your desired consistency.

3. Add in the essential oils and fully combine.

4. Store whipped lotions in a mason jar and thinner lotions in a pump container, out of direct sunlight. Use within 6 months.

PERSONALISED PERFUME

Perfume is such a personal thing.

Which is why we decided to put you in control of this DIY to create your own perfect scent. With a wealth of essential oils available, you could create a perfume for every occasion at a fraction of the cost. No more standing at the counter and sniffing endless samples. Once you've got the hang of it, this is simply a case of combining fragrances that you enjoy. However, we know that it can be daunting at first. So, we thought we would give you a little bit of guidance regarding base, middle and top notes, as well as the various base ingredients you can use.

Perfumer's Alcohol (denatured alcohol)

Denatured alcohol is an alcohol that has had poison added to it to prevent it from being consumed. This is done to protect tax revenue, despite the poisons often being carcinogenic or toxic to internal organs. The majority of the world's perfumes are made with this ingredient, as it's cheap and avoids alcohol taxation. So, when you enter the perfume area of a department store you are often breathing in toxic chemicals - then spraying these same chemicals onto your body. What better excuse is there to start making your own natural perfumes?

Alcohol

You can buy your own alcohol from a shop, which avoids having to add a denaturant since you've already paid the tax. The downside of this is that it increases the price of your project and the alcohol will add its own smell. The higher the alcohol content, the better it is at blending with fragrance - in the USA you can buy Everclear, or in Europe a high strength Russian vodka is normally used.

Cyclomethicone

A silicone oil like Cyclomethicone 5 works as a base ingredient - it's used by some aerosol brands. It blends essential oils well and evaporates quickly. It is a clear liquid and makes a great substitute, although it feels very different to a usual perfume - it makes skin slick and can also stain clothing. It has some downsides, but if you're keen on making perfume it's still worth trying out to see what you think.

Oil

Oil and water don't mix, so you can't make a water based perfume with essential oils. The easiest solution to this is to simply use oil as your base ingredient. Oil-based perfumes are 100% natural and Middle Eastern countries have been using them for years. They have some of the best perfumes in the world, but Western countries are still yet to catch on - partly because consumers simply aren't used to seeing them in the front of department stores. Using grapeseed oil as a base will allow you to blend any essential oils and create a totally natural perfume.

Perfume Notes

The longevity of your perfume will be based on the essential oils you use. Scents, in the perfume world, are referred to as base notes, middle notes and top notes. A base note has the longest lasting scent, while a top note has the shortest. All perfumes use a base note - patchouli and lavender are good examples - which you can then blend with top notes and middle notes to create your perfume. You can find our Essential Oils Guide on page 84, which tells you the perfume note of each oil.

Oil-Based Perfume

Create a natural perfume that's perfect to keep for yourself or give as a gift to others.

The strength of your perfume will largely depend on personal preference - it's a good idea to start with a blend and increase the ratio as you go until you reach your desired strength. As a guide, start with 5% essential oil, so 5ml of essential oil to 95ml of grapeseed oil.

Example Men's Pefume:	Example Women's Pefume:
Grapeseed oil 95ml	**Grapeseed oil** 95ml
Cedarwood essential oil 3ml	**Jasmine absolute oil** 6 drops
Patchouli essential oil 2ml	**Petitgrain essential oil** 1ml
Lavender essential oil 1ml	**Ylang ylang essential oil** 1ml

Method:

1. Pour the essential oils and carrier oil into your chosen bottle.

2. Shake to combine, then leave your perfume for about a week to allow the scents to combine and develop.

3. Enjoy making a variety of wonderful perfumes, whether for yourself or to give as gifts! Use within 12 months.

Helpful Hint: In the above blends the men's perfume will have a stronger scent of patchouli, while ylang ylang will stand out in the women's. Even though less of those oils are used, they have a more persistent scent than the others. The fun part of this hobby is working out which essential oils work well together, and how using different amounts changes the final outcome.

FLORAL DEODORANT

Most of us don't even think about what goes into our deodorants, but the reality can be pretty scary.

Knowing that the armpit contains a high concentration of lymph nodes, it's worrying to find out that conventional antiperspirants contain chemicals like aluminium which can seriously block your pores.

However, there is a natural alternative that will serve you just as well. By opting for a deodorant instead of an antiperspirant your armpits will be kept in tip top shape. This mix of lavender, chamomile and rose geranium will leave you smelling sweet and feeling secure all day long.

> ## Ingredients:
> **Coconut oil** 75g
> **Baking soda** 15g
> **Arrow root powder** 90g
> **Bentonite clay** 30g
> **Lavender essential oil** 5 drops
> **Chamomile essential oil** 2 drops
> **Rose geranium essential oil** 2 drops
> ## Equipment:
> **Microwave** or hob and pan
> **Small jar**

Method:

1. Melt the coconut oil in a pan, or in the microwave in 5 second intervals.

2. Add the essential oils to the coconut oil and mix until well combined.

3. Add the dry ingredients and stir until it forms a paste.

4. Store in a small jar, in cool environment.

5. To apply, simply scoop some from the jar and rub it under your armpits. It might seem messy to start with, but this product will revolutionise your daily routine! Use within 6 months and store in a dry, dark place.

BODY BUTTER BAR

Showering can be a lovely chance to unwind and de-stress.

This luxurious body butter bar is the perfect post-shower skin treat. It will leave your skin feeling soft, supple and richly moisturised, thanks to the heavenly combination of cocoa and shea butter.

The addition of clary sage gives this bar a fresh and sweet scent, while regulating dryness and working as an anti-inflammatory. The solid format makes this a quick and easy way to moisturise - perfect for those mornings when you don't have time to rub in lotion and wait for it to absorb. Instead of sacrificing moisturiser for a few extra minutes, simply swipe this bar across your skin and watch as the buttery formula melts in.

Ingredients:
Cocoa butter 50g
Shea butter 20g
Clary sage essential oil 10 drops

Equipment:
Hob and pan
Glass bowl
Mould

Method:

1. Melt the cocoa and shea butter together in a glass bowl, over a pan of boiling water.

2. Once fully melted, remove from the heat and add in the clary sage essential oil, stirring to combine.

3. Pour the mixture into your mould, and leave in the fridge to set.

4. Once fully set, remove from the mould. We recommend storing your bar in the fridge, in greaseproof paper to keep it clean.

5. Simply rub the bar across wet skin after the bath or shower to be left feeling wonderfully smooth! Use within 1 month.

THE RECIPES

BATH AND SHOWER

MUSCLE RELIEF BATH BOMBS

As if baths weren't relaxing enough already, these bath bombs use simple and natural ingredients to create a spa-like experience at home.

Once placed in the bath these beauties will fizz and eventually dissolve to leave the water any colour of your choice and the room filled with incredible scent. Although traditional bath bombs use ingredients such as boric acid which could be damaging to your health, it's easy to achieve the same result without that risk. This rosemary and eucalyptus bath bomb is perfect for relief from sore muscles. However, the possibilities are endless. Use our Essential Oils Guide on page 84 to create the mix that suits you. If you're looking for a relaxing bath, why not try lavender? Or if it's invigoration you're after, opt for citrus oils instead.

Method:

1. Sieve the citric acid and bicarbonate of soda into the bowl and mix together thoroughly.

2. Add the food colouring to the mix one drop at a time until you get your desired colour, stirring quickly to avoid fizzing.

3. Mix in the essential oils quickly and thoroughly to avoid fizzing.

4. Carefully spray small amounts of water into the mixture in intervals, until it starts to hold together when pressed in your hand.

5. Quickly transfer the mixture into your spherical moulds, filling each half and then pressing the two together for around 20 seconds.

6. Gently remove one half of the mould, then leave the bath bombs to set for about 30 minutes in a cool, dry environment.

7. Test to see if they are solid enough, before removing the rest of the mould.

8. Once removed, leave the loose bath bombs to completely dry before use. Use within 1 month and store in a dry place.

Ingredients:
Citric acid 100g
Bicarbonate of soda 300g
Rosemary essential oil 1/2 tbsp (7.5ml)
Eucalyptus essential oil 1/2 tsp (2.5ml)
Food colouring of your choice
Equipment:
Large mixing bowl
Spherical or two-part moulds
Spray bottle filled with water

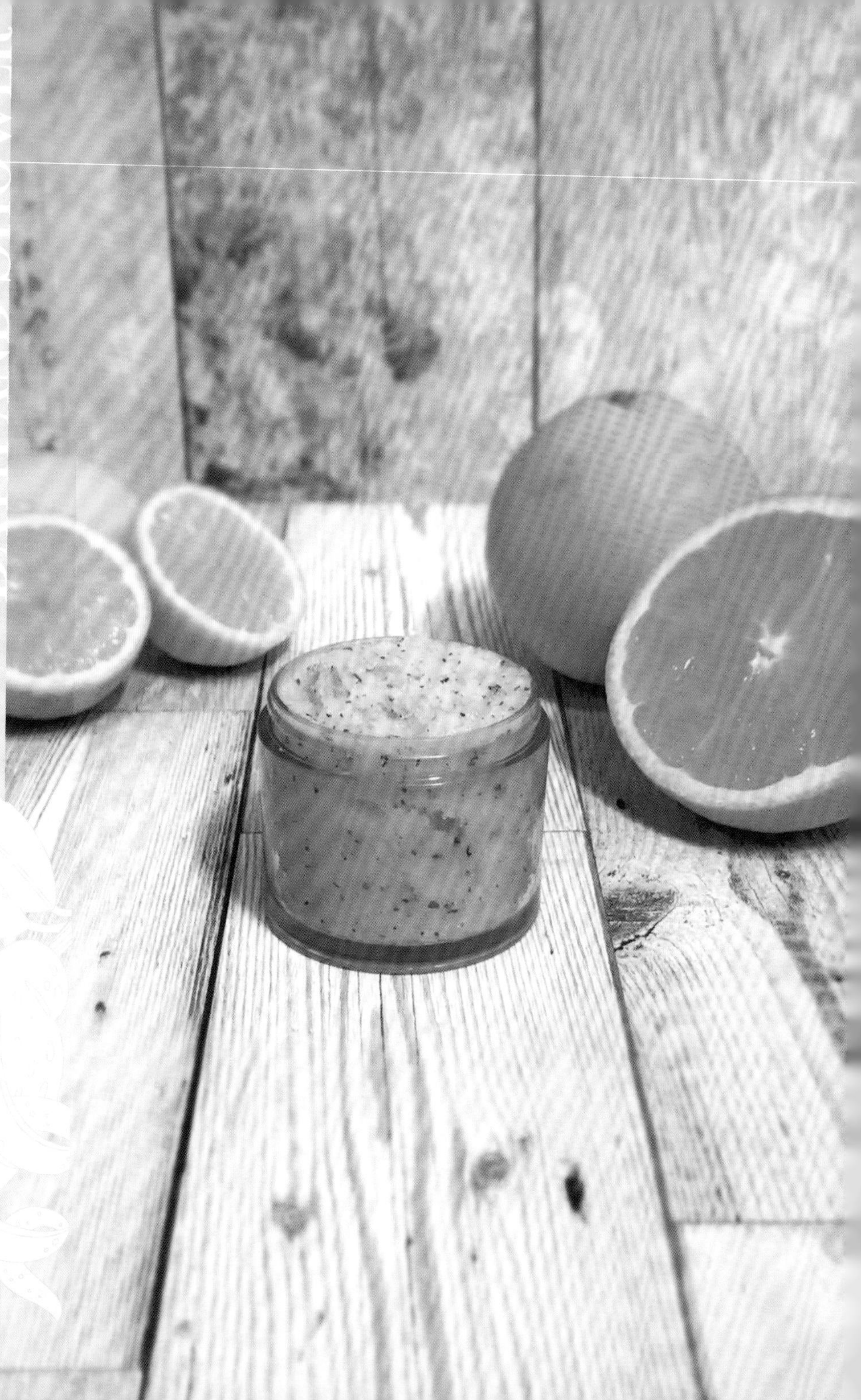

CITRUS AND GREEN TEA BODY SCRUB

A good body scrub should be a part of everyone's shower routine.

Not only will it leave you silky smooth, but buffing away dead skin cells will make you glow like nothing else. The best part is that they are extremely easy to make, saving you money and allowing you to adapt the consistency to your preference. The mix of citrus and green tea makes this a perfect wake up call for the body. This scrub is coarse so is perfect for use on dry feet or any areas that need a little bit of extra love.

Ingredients:
Granulated sugar 300g
Oil (of your choice) 100g
Orange essential oil 1 tsp (5ml)
Lemon essential oil 1 tsp (5ml)
Green tea bag (contents)
Lime zest 1 tsp
Equipment:
Bowl
Spoon
Airtight container

Method:

1. Combine all of the ingredients and mix thoroughly.

2. If you feel as though the mixture is too wet, add more sugar for a coarser scrub. To make the mixture less harsh, add more of the oil of your choice.

3. To store the mixture, keep it in an airtight container such as a mason jar. Use within 1 month.

Intensive Hair Conditioning Mask

Heat, air pollution and styling can seriously damage hair, leaving it dry and prone to breakage.

Due to this it's important to pamper it every now and then with an intensive conditioning mask, to return it to its former glory. The best ingredient for damaged hair is oil, particularly coconut oil, which is also a great remedy for dandruff. This hair mask combines the wonder of coconut oil with lavender essential oil. That way, you get a salon-like treatment and a relaxing aromatherapy session, too!

Ingredients:
Coconut oil 45g
Extra virgin olive oil 1 tbsp (15ml)
Lavender essential oil 8 drops
Equipment:
Large bowl
Electric whisk
Airtight container (such as a mason jar)

Method:

1. Using the electric whisk, combine all of the ingredients on a medium speed until it forms a thick, whipped consistency.

2. Store in an air tight container.

3. To use, simply comb this through your hair, focusing on the ends and leave it for 30 minutes.

4. Rinse out with shampoo and style as desired. Use within 1 month.

WAKE ME UP
SHOWER JELLY

Showers are a part of life that most of us do half-asleep, but we promise that these shower jellies are going to change that!

A fun take on traditional shower gels, these invigorating jellies wibble and wobble as you use them. Simply wet and rub one over your skin, or chop them up and rub individual chunks into your loofa to use like a normal gel. The mix of orange and lemon is bound to wake you up in the morning and leave you as clean as a whistle.

Method:

1. Mix the agar-agar powder and boiling water, until completely dissolved.

2. Microwave the melt and pour soap for 20 seconds, until completely liquid.

3. Add the soap to the agar mix and stir thoroughly.

4. Add the essential oils and quickly mix until combined.

5. Mix in the salt.

6. Pour the mixture into your silicone moulds carefully. It can be helpful to put the moulds onto a tray prior to filling for easy transportation.

7. Leave in the fridge to completely set and then remove from the moulds.

8. Store the jellies in the fridge in an air tight container. Use within 1 month.

Ingredients:
Powdered agar-agar 25g
Boiling water 170ml
Melt and pour soap compound 20g
Orange essential oil 3 drops
Lemon essential oil 3 drops
Salt 1 tsp
Colouring (of your choice)

Equipment:
Glass jug
Microwave
Silicone moulds

Rosemary and Cedarwood Shampoo

Conventional detergent shampoos can strip the hair of its natural oils, as well as being harmful to the water's ecosystems.

By ditching the chemicals and opting instead for this homemade version, you can take care of your hair without the need for parabens and sulphates. Rice milk and rosemary oil each contain vitamins that encourage hair growth, whilst cedarwood reduces scalp dryness.

Ingredients:
Rice milk 230ml
Melt and pour soap compound 75g
Cedarwood essential oil 5 drops
Rosemary essential oil 5 drops
Equipment:
Microwave
Funnel
Squeeze or pump bottle

Method:

1. Microwave the melt and pour soap for 1 minute until completely liquid.

2. Pour the rice milk and melt and pour soap in your bowl and stir until completely combined.

3. Add in the cedarwood and rosemary essential oils and stir.

4. Place the funnel into your bottle and pour in the shampoo.

5. If separation occurs, simply shake before use. Use within 1 month and store in the fridge.

GROWTH STIMULATING SCALP SCRUB

This scalp scrub is the answer for anybody looking to grow long luscious locks, or free themselves from dry and flaky skin.

Granulated sugar helps to reduce product build up, as well as stimulating blood flow to the scalp in order to encourage hair growth. We recommend adding chamomile oil to soothe the scalp and avoid making the scrub too harsh. It won't turn you into Rapunzel overnight, but with repeated use you're sure to see the benefits!

Ingredients:
Sugar 45g
Grapeseed oil 2 tbsp (30ml)
Chamomile essential oil 5 drops
Equipment:
Spoon
Jar

Method:

1. Combine the grapeseed oil and chamomile in a jar and shake to mix.

2. Stir in the sugar until the mixture holds together.

3. Either use immediately or store in an air tight container.

4. Stir the scrub before use, then massage into the scalp after washing and rinse away. Use within 1 month and store in a dry place.

Personalised Soaps

If you think that making your own cosmetics is fiddly and difficult, this DIY is about to change your life.

In a few easy steps, you can create something that looks like it was bought from a cosmetics boutique, but for a lot less money and without having to leave your kitchen. When making soaps we highly recommend opting for the melt and pour method, for the sake of ease and safety. That way, you can focus on creating colours, shapes, scents and toppings that you enjoy. Basically, you get to do all of the fun stuff, without the hassle.

Ingredients:
Melt and pour soap compound 500g
Essential oils (of your choice) 2 tsp (10ml)
Colourants
Toppings (if desired)
Equipment:
Microwave
Bowl
Mixing spoon
Moulds

Method:

1. Place your melt and pour compound into the bowl and microwave in 2 minute intervals.

2. Once completely liquid, add any colourants and essential oils that you desire, then stir until fully combined.

3. Pour the soap mixture into the moulds and sprinkle over any toppings you are using. Leave the soaps for 2 to 3 hours to allow them to set.

4. Once the soaps are fully set, remove them from the moulds and they will be immediately ready for use! Use within 12 months.

Scents:

This is a chance to really get creative, so don't shy away from trying different essential oils, using our guide on page 84.

Tea tree oil is a great option for hand soaps as it has antimicrobial properties to keep bad bacteria at bay. Alternatively, peppermint and orange create a fresh scent that is perfect for keeping by the sink.

Moulds:

Although it can be tempting to invest in fancy silicone moulds for your soaps, that is not the only option. Simply line any household container with clingfilm to create your own moulds at a fraction of the price.

Toppings:

To give your soaps a professional look, top them with dried flowers, cinnamon sticks, or dried fruit and wrap them in brown paper and string.

Colouring:

You can invest in natural colourants, using our guide on page 14. For example, wheatgrass can make a gorgeous light green colour which is especially good for mint scented soaps.

Ingredients:
Baking soda 250g
Citric acid 125g
Corn starch 60g
Coconut oil 60g
Chamomile essential oil 7 drops
Lavender essential oil 3 drops
Chamomile tea (contents of 2 bags)
Equipment:
Silicone ice cube mould (that holds 10-15)
Airtight container or bag

Soothing Chamomile Shower Fizzers

You know those days when all you want to do is have a long soak in the bath, with a book and a glass of the good stuff, but life just laughs in your face and hands you your to-do list?

This is the recipe for those days. Those days when time just forces you to settle for a shower. Trust us though, these aromatherapy fizzers will leave you wondering why you were so fussed about having a bath in the first place. Thanks to the power of lavender and chamomile, you can turn your shower into a five-minute spa session that will help to release tension and clear your mind. Although, we can't promise that those five minutes won't turn into ten!

Method:

1. Combine your baking soda, citric acid and corn starch, then mix together with a hand whisk.

2. Add in your coconut oil and mix, bringing the dry ingredients together until it resembles something like chunky bread crumbs.

3. Mix in the essential oils and then add your chamomile tea. This will create texture and make the fizzers look extra pretty if you want to give them as gifts.

4. Pack the mixture into silicone moulds. Make sure to press it down firmly and then leave to dry for 24 hours.

5. Turn the moulds out and store in an air tight container or bag to keep them strong and smelling sweet.

6. To use your luxurious new fizzers, just place them in the base of your shower, preferably out of the direct water stream. Use within 1 month.

Helpful Hint: The larger you make these fizzers, the longer they will last. Those made in the average ice cube mould will fizz away for around 5 minutes each, but the gorgeous scent will last for a lot longer!

BATH SALTS

Having a bath is already a wonderful experience, immersing yourself in warm, relaxing water.

But you can make it even better with the use of natural mineral salts. The two most popular options are epsom salt and dead sea salt. Epsom salts are a great muscle relaxant, perfect for relieving tension after that long jog or gym session, while dead sea salts are used for detoxifying and softening skin. This is one of the simplest DIYs you can do - the only hard part is choosing which salts and essential oils to use!

Ingredients:
Dead sea salt 250g
or
Epsom salt 250g
Essential oil (of your choice) 5-10 drops
Equipment:
Airtight container
Spoon

Method:

1. Pour your chosen salt into your container.

2. Drip your essential oil in and stir well.

3. Dissolve the full amount in your bath for a relaxing soak. Use within 1 month and store in a dry place.

Bee-Free Lavender Bath Melts

If you want a multitasking product, these bath melts are for you.

Not only will they help to eliminate stress with their soothing lavender scent, but they will deeply nourish your skin. The best part? All of it's done in the bath. As soon as you step out you don't even have to think about body butters or moisturisers. Their gentle mix of essential oils and coconut oil makes them one of the simplest but most effective recipes in this book. You'll find a lot of homemade cosmetics use beeswax, but this can often be replaced by coconut oil for a nice vegan alternative. Within a few hours you'll have little blocks of nourishment, ready to be popped in your bath water and leave you feeling super smooth!

Ingredients:
Coconut oil 250g
Lavender essential oil 16 drops
Dried flowers or herbal tea (optional)
Equipment:
Ice cube mould (preferably silicone)
Hob and pan

Method:

1. Melt your coconut oil over the hob on a low heat until it's liquid.

2. Take the coconut oil off the heat and add your essential oils before mixing well to ensure they are evenly distributed.

3. Carefully pour your oil mixture into a mould. It may help to decant the liquid into a jug with a lip beforehand.

Optional: Sprinkle in your dried flowers or herbal tea to add texture.

4. Leave the mould in the fridge for a couple of hours or until it's solid.

5. Simply pop the melts out and they are ready to work their magic! Use within 1 week.

Helpful Hint:
For an invigorating bath, you can try using citrus essential oils instead!

The Recipes

The Home

ORANGE AND PATCHOULI REED DIFFUSER

Reed diffusers are an amazing way to create an inviting space and turn your home into your own sanctuary.

This simple DIY will help to lift the mood of any room and is an eco-friendly alternative to plug-in air fresheners. This reed diffuser uses base notes of patchouli, which will save you spending on endless plug-in refills thanks to its scent longevity. Plus, since we know that conventional air fresheners are filled with potentially damaging chemicals, there's never been a better time to make this natural switch. The uplifting top note of orange elevates this mix and completes the scent that will become a staple in your home.

Ingredients:
Carrier oil, silicone oil, or alcohol 90ml (90%)
Essential oils 10ml (10%): **Patchouli** 6ml **Orange** 4ml
Equipment:
Glass bottle or jar (tall enough for reeds to stand in)
Wooden reeds 4-10
Glass jug

Method:

1. Mix your carrier oil and essential oils in the glass jug, making sure that they are fully combined.

2. Pour the mixture into your glass bottle, leaving a suitable amount of space at the top to allow for the reeds.

3. Push your reeds into the glass. The more reeds you use, the stronger the scent will be, as more oil will be dispersed. Use within 12 months.

Helpful Hint: The best part is that this recipe is simply your starting point. As you get more confident and grow your oil collection you can create new fragrances, sticking to the 90% carrier oil to 10% essential oil ratio.

PEPPERMINT AND ORANGE WAX MELTS

Wax melts are a fun alternative to conventional candles that let you explore endless shapes, colours and scent combinations to suit your personal taste.

Simply place these individual wax cubes into the top of an oil burner with a tea light underneath. Once melted they will release enough scent to fill a whole room. With top notes of peppermint and orange this blend is invigorating and perfect to keep you motivated and focused!
The power is in your hands. However, we recommend using soy wax as the most eco-friendly option. When buying your wax ensure that you get 'pillar blend', which shrinks slightly when set to make them easy to remove from moulds. Always be careful when working with hot wax – this is meant to be a fun and creative DIY, we don't want any injuries!

Method:

1. Put the soy wax in your bowl and microwave it for 30 seconds at a time, until it is liquid and has a temperature of around 85°C. Alternatively, do this in a glass bowl over a pan of boiling water.

2. Add the essential oils (and dyes if desired) to your wax and mix until it is all combined and one solid colour.

3. Leave your mixture to cool until it reaches roughly 60°C to avoid the melts dipping in the middle.

4. Carefully pour the wax into your moulds.

5. Leave your melts to completely set in a cool dry environment. This could take a few days.

6. Once they are cooled and completely set, pop them out of the moulds and they are ready to use. Use within 12 months.

Helpful Hint: If you want to make your wax melts look even more professional, sprinkle on some dried citrus peels between steps 4 and 5.

Ingredients:
Soy 'pillar blend' wax 100g
Peppermint essential oil 20 drops
Orange essential oil 1 tsp (5ml)
Candle dye (optional)
Equipment:
Large microwavable bowl or jug
Thermometer
Moulds (ice cube or small baking moulds
will work)
Microwave or hob and pan

Blue Lotus Absolute Room Spray

Absolutes, much like essential oils, are extracted from plants to leave us with an aromatic liquid.

However, there is a lengthy and complex process to extracting absolutes that means they have longevity and a stronger scent. Although they are more expensive than conventional oils, they are often favoured due to their intense and rare qualities. Blue lotus was considered sacred to the Ancient Egyptians thanks to the blissful and spiritual experiences it evoked. Today, it is still enjoyed as a therapeutic oil, making the perfect addition to any home. This room spray makes enjoying the benefits of blue lotus easy. Use daily to improve the atmosphere of your home whilst also expelling odours from pets, cooking or day to day life.

Ingredients:
Witch hazel with alcohol 2 tbsp (30ml)
Distilled water 90ml
Blue lotus absolute 2 drops
Equipment:
Airtight jar
Funnel
Small spray bottle

Method:

1. Combine the witch hazel and blue lotus in the jar, screw on the lid and shake well for around 30 seconds.

2. Add the water to the mix, replace the lid and shake again for 30 seconds.

3. Place the funnel inside the spray bottle and pour the liquid in.

4. Shake the bottle before use. There is no emulsifier in this product so it will need to be mixed first. Use within 3 months.

ALL PURPOSE CLEANING SPRAY

These days it seems like there's a cleaning product for every item in the home.

Not only can that be overwhelming, but it is also totally unnecessary. This all-purpose cleaning spray will save you money, reduce plastic waste and work wonders on every surface. Tea tree and lemon essential oils are natural disinfectants that also leave the room smelling fresh. Combined with the brightening and odour eliminating properties of vinegar, this spray is a powerful bathroom and kitchen companion.

Ingredients:
Vinegar 250ml
Distilled water 250ml
Lemon essential oil 20 drops
Tea tree essential oil 20 drops
Polysorbate 20 emulsifier 30g
Equipment:
Glass spray bottle

Method:

1. Combine all of the ingredients in the spray bottle and shake well.
2. Spray on your surface and wipe away with a clean, dry cloth or sponge.
3. Store your spray in a cool place, out of direct sunlight and shake well before every use. Use within 3 months.

AROMATHERAPY CANDLES

We've saved the most difficult DIY until last, but it's also the most rewarding. Many people choose this as a full time hobby and it's one that pays off all year round, especially as gifts to family and friends.

In the UK alone more than £90 million a year is spent on candles and it's easy to understand why. They can make a room feel cosier in seconds. If you want to fuel your love for cosy nights in without the hefty price tag, you should definitely try your hand at making your own.

With a bit of patience and practice you will find creating your own candles easy. Plus, unlike shop-bought alternatives, this gives you the opportunity to mix scents that you love.

Ingredients:
Soy wax flakes container blend
Waxed candle wicks
Wax dye blocks (optional but gorgeous)
Essential oils (of your choice)
Equipment:
Containers for your candles
Skewers or straws
Tape and scissors
Hob and pan
Old glass bowl or jug

Method:

1. Ensure that your containers are ready to be filled prior to starting by sticking the metal plate of your wicks to the bottom of them with a dot of glue. It can help to hold the wicks up by taping them to a skewer and placing it across the top of the container.

2. Measure out enough wax flakes to fill your container twice. Once this is melted down you should be left with the perfect amount.

3. Add the wax flakes and any colouring to the glass bowl.

4. Place the bowl over a pan of simmering water and stir occasionally with a metal spoon. Remove it from the hob once the wax is completely melted.

5. The optimum temperature to add your essential oils is 70°C. We recommend using about 16 drops of oil per 450g of wax.

6. Make sure your containers are out of the way and won't need to be moved for a few hours, then carefully pour your wax into each container.

7. Allow the candles to cool at room temperature to avoid the wax cracking.

8. Smaller candles will take around 2 hours to set, whilst larger ones could take upwards of 4 hours.

9. Once completely set, simply light the wicks and bask in the cosiness! Use within 12 months.

AROMATHERAPY GUIDE

A GUIDE TO AROMATHERAPY

Of our five senses, scent is often overlooked. However, it can have a marvellous effect on our health, body and mind. Imagine how you feel when you smell your favourite food (pancakes, Sunday dinner, baked bread). Something as simple as this can transport us to a memory, or provide us with a sense of happiness and security. This itself can have healing powers on the body and mind.

Aromatherapists use natural aromas (mainly plant extracted essential oils) to help with holistic healing. However, you don't have to be an aromatherapist to use essential oils at home. Many of the health properties of essential oils can be experienced through simple activities or applications.

Lots of the recipes in this book make use of aromatherapy - like our Dreamy Lavender and Orange Lotion (page 36) which uses the calming effect of lavender and anxiety-reducing power of orange to relax you before bed. Or our Tea Tree Spot Stick (page 18) which uses the antibacterial and antiseptic properties of tea tree essential oil to fight spots.

AROMATHERAPY MASSAGE

One of the easiest ways to experience the benefits of aromatherapy is with an aromatherapy massage oil. Whether you massage yourself or receive a massage from someone else, it can be a relaxing experience that helps to relieve tension and ease the mind.

Massage is one of the best ways to experience the benefits of essential oils, as it boosts circulation and the warmth of skin makes the scent stronger - meaning you receive quicker therapeutic benefits to body and mind. For the most comfortable experience you should make sure your massage oil is warm. You can do this by placing the container in hot water for a few minutes.

Your aromatherapy oil can have a relaxing or stimulating effect, depending on the oils you use. Over the next few pages we will explore the different essential oils and the effects they can have on the body and mind. To learn how to make your own, turn to page 34 for our 'Sensual Massage Oil' recipe.

SAFETY WITH ESSENTIAL OILS

Although essential oils are the key to making amazing smelling products, when not diluted they are very strong and potentially harmful. For this reason, it is important to follow these safety guidelines when making any of the products in this book.

Essential oils should never be used neat on the skin and products containing essential oils should not be applied to sensitive or broken skin. If irritation occurs, wash off with clean water and soap immediately and, if it persists, seek medical advice.
These products are for external use only and contact with the eyes should be avoided at all times. Do not use essential oil products on children, when pregnant or whilst using medication. Keep all bottles on high shelves out of reach from children and pets. Essential oils are not an alternative to seeking medical help and guidance. Do not self-prescribe and, when in doubt, always talk to your doctor.

Essential Oils Guide

Essential oils are one of the best natural cosmetic ingredients available and we think the whole world should be using them. These little miracle drops are a power product that can do so much more than just smell nice. Whether it's for concentration, detoxification, clearer skin or stress reduction, there's an oil for everything.

Recently, people have really started to become more aware of what they're putting on their skin. Gone are the days when brands could get away with having ingredients lists longer than your arm, full of words that you wouldn't even want to attempt to pronounce. People are starting to take matters into their own hands by jumping into the wonderful world of homemade cosmetics. We're glad to see people ditching the shop bought products in favour of organic, DIY cosmetics that incorporate essential oils. We love that the world is learning just how life changing they can be! But we also know that it can be pretty overwhelming when you first start exploring how to use them - that's where this book comes in to help.

Let's start with the basics! To get from plant or seed to sweet smelling bottle, essential oil manufacturers use distillation. Not only does this get rid of impurities, but it means that the oils are characterised by the scent of the plant that they come from. A lot of raw materials are needed in the process so essential oils are powerful little things, with a small amount of product going a long way. Of course, that's one of their main benefits, but due to their strength it's also important to understand that essential oils should never be used neat on the skin. Don't worry, we've got plenty of helpful advice and glorious DIYs throughout this book to help you dip your toes into the world of natural cosmetics. The following guide to essential oils provides you with information on the scents, properties, perfume notes and aromatherapy benefits of 26 of the most popular essential oils and absolutes.

BERGAMOT

Uses: A relaxing, refreshing and uplifting aroma. It can help with skin conditions such as acne, eczema and cold sores.

Botanical Name, Origin: *Citrus bergamia*, Italy

Description: The Bergamot tree is a native of Southern Italy and produces fruits. The oil is expressed from these fruits.

Aromatic Scent: A lemony fresh smell with balsamic undertones.

Perfume Note: Middle to Top

BLUE LOTUS ABSOLUTE

Uses: Often used in the perfume industry, this is an aphrodisiac and provides a feeling of euphoria.

Botanical Name, Origin: *Nymphaea Caerulea*, Egypt

Description: Comes from the lotus plant. This is an absolute oil, extracted using alcohol.

Aromatic Scent: An addictively beautiful and sweet smelling oil.

Perfume Note: Middle

CAJUPUT

Uses: This oil is a great decongestant, when used carefully and in moderation. It is also helpful in the relief of aches and pains. Combine the oil with a cream to help alleviate skin conditions.

Botanical Name, Origin: *Melaleuca leucadendron*, Indonesia

Description: Comes from the white tea tree, where the oil is extracted from leaves and twigs.

Aromatic Scent: A strong medicinal smell, with a woody aroma.

Perfume Note: Top

CEDARWOOD

Uses: Relieves itching and is good for oily skin and hair conditions. Its calming and soothing properties help relieve nerves and anxiety conditions.

Botanical Name, Origin: *Cedrus deodara*, India

Description: Woodchips and sawdust are steam distilled to extract the oil.

Aromatic Scent: A dry and woody scent, with a balsamic undertone.

Perfume Note: Base

CHAMOMILE

Uses: This oil has calming properties that can contribute to easing irritability and reducing stress levels. It can relieve PMS and allergies such as itchy skin and dermatitis. A great alternative to lavender.

Botanical Name, Origin: *Anthemis nobilis*, England

Description: The oil is extracted from the hairy stems of a low growing flower (like a daisy).

Aromatic Scent: Fruity and sweet scent with a hint of apple.

Perfume Note: Middle to Top, herbaceous top with a sweeter middle.

CINNAMON

Uses: Stimulating, has been known to increase work productivity. Use sparingly and with care, a little goes a long way with this strong aroma. Do not use in skin products as it can cause sensitivity.

Botanical Name, Origin: *Cinnamomum zeylanicum*, Sri Lanka

Description: Extracted from bark of the tree.

Aromatic Scent: Spicy and fiery with oriental aromas. Slightly less sweet than cinnamon powder.

Perfume Note: Base to Top

CITRONELLA

Uses: Mixed with cream or lotion, it is a great feet freshener. Used in cosmetics to fight perspiration and oily skin, also used in wax candles and diffusers. It is a good muscle relaxant.

Botanical Name, Origin:
Cymbopogon winteratus, Indonesia

Description: The oil comes from the andropogon nardus plant which is distilled from the dry grass. Can be slightly irritating to very sensitive skin.

Aromatic Scent: Sweet, lemony aroma.

Perfume Note: Middle to Top

CLARY SAGE

Uses: It can regulate skin dryness and works as an anti-inflammatory. It is an aphrodisiac and can ease the symptoms of period pain, however it should not be used during pregnancy.

Botanical Name, Origin: *Salvia Sclarea*, France

Description: The oil comes from the leaves of the colourful flowering sage plant in Europe.

Aromatic Scent: One of the sweeter herbaceous aromas with a unique freshness.

Perfume Note: Middle to Top

EUCALYPTUS

Uses: Clears your sinuses and can be good for respiratory problems. It is commonly used in cold remedies.

Botanical Name, Origin: *Eucalyptus Globulus*, China

Description: The oil comes from small white and yellow flowers and the leaves from evergreen trees.

Aromatic Scent: Herbaceous with slight menthol undertones. Very strong scent.

Perfume Note: Top

FRANKINCENSE

Uses: Stimulates a person's mind and provides a feeling of comfort and rejuvenation. Can be great at repairing skin and is often used on scars.
Botanical Name, Origin: *Boswellia carterii*, India
Description: The oil comes from the bark of a small shrubby tree.
Aromatic Scent: A unique, fresh citrus scent with woody, spicy balsamic undertones.
Perfume Note: Base

GERANIUM

Uses: It can soothe skin and relieve anxiety. A balancing essential oil that mixes well with clary sage and can be good for menopausal problems. Can help regulate the hormonal system.
Botanical Name, Origin:
Pelargonium x asperum, Egypt
Description: The oil comes from the flowers, leaves and stalks of an evergreen shrub.
Aromatic Scent: Strong green floral scent with earthy undertones.
Perfume Note: Middle to Top

GRAPEFRUIT

Uses: Uplifting and refreshing. Typically used to help with fatigue, hangovers and headaches.
Botanical Name, Origin: *Citrus paradisi*, Israel
Description: The oil comes from the peel of the fruit that is grown on a glossy leaved tree.
Aromatic Scent: A sweet and fruity scent, with an uplifting and refreshing aroma.
Perfume Note: Top

Jasmine Absolute

Uses: Known to be an aphrodisiac and can be used in meditation to help with reducing habits and ticks.
Botanical Name, Origin:
Jasminun grandiflorum, India
Description: It is an absolute solvent extraction.
Aromatic Scent: Sweet and musky perfume scent, with a dark base note.
Perfume Note: Base

Juniper

Uses: Clearing and refreshing, often used in mens' perfumes. Acts as an emmenagogue (stimulates menstruation) so should be kept away from pregnant women. Essential oils should never be used on pregnant women.
Botanical Name, Origin:
Juniperus communis, Napal
Description: The oil comes from the berries of an evergreen shrub.
Aromatic Scent: The oil has a fresh aroma with notes of turpentine, pepper and balsamic undertones.
Perfume Note: Middle to Top

Lavender

Uses: Lavender is an antiseptic. Acts as a stimulant while having a relaxing effect. It is great for bedtime use, drop it on the radiator before you fall asleep.
Botanical Name, Origin:
Lavendula angustifolia, France
Description: Comes from the leaves and spiky flowers of a shrub.
Aromatic Scent: A clean and fresh floral scent.
Perfume Note: Top

LEMON

Uses: Invigorating and deodorising.
Botanical Name, Origin: *Citrus limonum*, Italy
Description: The oil comes from the green and yellow fruits of a thorny evergreen tree.
Aromatic Scent: Lemon and citrus.
Perfume Note: Top

LEMONGRASS

Uses: Invigorating aroma for the home, with anti fungal and antibacterial properties.
Botanical Name, Origin: *Cymbopogon flexuosus*, India
Description: The oil is taken from the leaves of a herb grown in India.
Aromatic Scent: A strong, sweet lemony scent.
Perfume Note: Middle to Top

LIME

Uses: It has a stimulating effect on the mind.
Botanical Name, Origin: *Citrus aurantifolia*, Peru
Description: The oil comes from the peel of the fruit which grows from a small evergreen tree.
Aromatic Scent: Sharp citrus peel aroma.
Perfume Note: Top

ORANGE

Uses: Refreshes and stimulates. Can rejuvenate the skin, but should avoid using in direct sunlight as it can sensitise the skin for a few hours after use.
Botanical Name, Origin: *Citrus sinensis*, Brazil
Description: This oil is expressed from the peel of the citrus fruit.
Aromatic Scent: A fruity, sweet orange scent.
Perfume Note: Top

PATCHOULI

Uses: It is an anti-inflammatory and an aphrodisiac, often used in a perfume as a base note. It mixes wonderfully with other floral top notes, like ylang ylang.
Botanical Name, Origin: *Pogostemon cablin*, Indonesia
Description: The oil comes from the leaves of flowers which grow from aromatic tall grass.
Aromatic Scent: A strong earthy scent.
Perfume Note: Base

PEPPERMINT

Uses: Peppermint refreshes and soothes. The menthol aroma stimulates your mind. Do not use in massage oils as it can have a tingling effect on the skin.
Botanical Name, Origin: *Mentha piperita*, India
Description: A fast growing herb with small white flowers.
Aromatic Scent: Minty fresh scent.
Perfume Note: Top

PETITGRAIN

Uses: Helps to reduce stress and build confidence. The aroma provides a fresh atmosphere around the wearer.
Botanical Name, Origin: *Citrus uranium*, France
Description: Taken from the twigs and leaves of the bitter orange tree.
Aromatic Scent: A fresh, green scent with hints of floral notes, mixed with balsamic and woody undertones.
Perfume Note: Top, but has persistence in blends.

ROSE GERANIUM

Uses: Can relieve anxiety. A balancing oil that can be good for menopausal problems. Can help regulate the hormonal system.
Botanical Name, Origin: *Pelargonium roseum*, South Africa
Description: The oil comes from the flowering plant.
Aromatic Scent: A rosy, floral balancing scent.
Perfume Note: Top, with green herbal Base notes.

ROSEMARY

Uses: The oil is cleansing, invigorating and stimulating.
Botanical Name, Origin:
Rosmarinus officinalis, Tunisia
Description: The oil is steam distilled from the flowering tops and leaves of the 'sea dew' (Latin for rosemary).
Aromatic Scent: A green woody and minty aroma. A subtle alternative to peppermint if you still require a fresh minty aroma.
Perfume Note: Middle

TEA TREE

Uses: Is an antiseptic oil that can help to fight bacteria, fungi and viruses. Can help to fight acne.
Botanical Name, Origin:
Melaleuca alternifolia, Australia
Description: The oil comes from a small tree (similar to Cypress) in the marshy areas of Australia.
Aromatic Scent: Medicinal with a long lasting, refreshing scent.
Perfume Note: Middle to Top

YLANG YLANG

Uses: Can promote confidence and is great for helping to reduce anxiety. The oil is used in perfumes due to its beautiful scent. Acts as an emmenagogue so should be kept away from pregnant women.
Botanical Name, Origin:
Cananga odorata, Madagascar
Description: A brittle orange tree produces small white flowers that are steam distilled for the oil.
Aromatic Scent: Sweet floral.
Perfume Note: Base to Middle

Aromatherapy Map Of Essential Oils

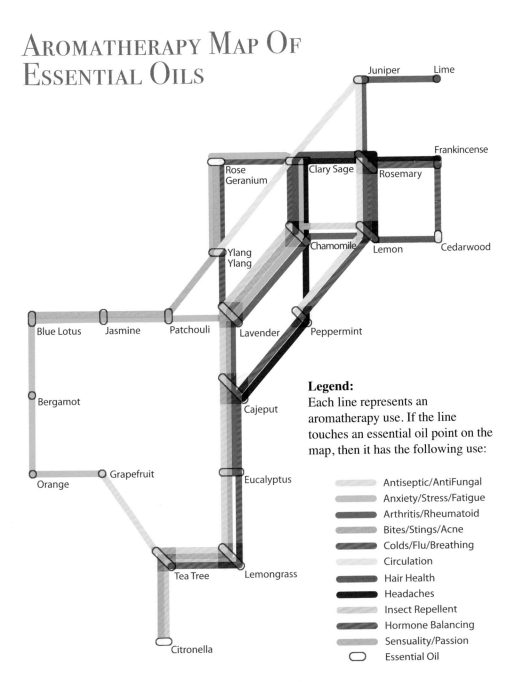

Legend:
Each line represents an aromatherapy use. If the line touches an essential oil point on the map, then it has the following use:

- Antiseptic/AntiFungal
- Anxiety/Stress/Fatigue
- Arthritis/Rheumatoid
- Bites/Stings/Acne
- Colds/Flu/Breathing
- Circulation
- Hair Health
- Headaches
- Insect Repellent
- Hormone Balancing
- Sensuality/Passion
- Essential Oil

Map shows the most popular properties associated with each oil.
i.e. Lavender has more uses but this map shows the most common properties.

All these oils are available to purchase from www.tenderessence.com
© Copyright Tender Essence. Created 2014.

Acknowledgments

Bethany Austin for her fantastic research skills and writing the vast majority of this book. Thank you.

Abigail Mays for "getting on with it" and giving us that final design masterpiece. Well done.

Laura Long, Louise Keable and Octavia India Brown, for their feedback, inspirational ideas and photographs. The best team anyone could ask for.

Adele Rudge for her patience and editorial work.

Work placement students from Selby College for illustrations, recipe testing and further photography.

Tender Essence and its staff for all the equipment and ingredients needed.

All items found in this book can be purchased from www.tenderessence.com

David Brennan for his green thinking and dedication to the idea that cosmetics don't have to contain animals.

All things bright and beautiful,
All creatures great and small,
All things wise and wonderful,
The Lord God made them all.

Each little flower that opens,
Each little bird that sings,
He made their glowing colours,
He made their tiny wings.

- Cecil Frances Alexander

THANK YOU FOR YOUR SUPPORT

We hope this book has inspired you to create your own natural products and that you continue to enjoy this rewarding experience.

All the ingredients used in this book are available to buy at:
www.tenderessence.com